Be kind to yourself, you are enough.

To love oneself is the beginning of a lifelong romance.

OSCAR WILDE

Introducing
the "Philosophy of You"

The origin story of our company is a sad one, most origin stories are. However, if you immediately thought of Batman, or Bambi, (spoiler alert) it got better. Our story starts with a 40 year-old guy who had what everyone - including himself - saw as the perfect life: a family, ideal friends, a designer home and a dream job, but he decided to move abroad and risk it all. Why? Because he felt that there was more to life waiting for him, he was still too young to settle for less than "awesome."

He asked himself, "what would you do if you could write the next chapter of your life with absolute freedom? No one to answer but yourself and nothing to fulfill except your own dreams." We spend most of our lives doing what others expect of us or, even worse, what we think they expect. Oftentimes, it turns out not to be true. So what would he achieve and who would he become without society holding him back?

The protagonist of this brief tale soon discovered he could not answer these questions. He didn't know what he expected from himself outside of society's expectations. Nonetheless, our guy knew this version of himself wasn't good for his health and that he had to evolve. He eventually realized that this crisis was actually an opportunity (he really should have seen this coming) to overcome his years of confusion and emerge as a new person who radiates authenticity. He had to revisit every aspect of his life and cast a shadow of doubt on everything he used to hold sacred to experience his new dreams come to life.

Everything in his life started making sense after he found clarity and decided what he wanted and who he desired to be. Life began to flow easier and faster as the protagonist learned to appreciate himself and his life. Then, Youlosophy was born. It's a "lab for personal innovation" with the sole mission of triggering inner searches of purpose and empowering people to dream big again.

We have hosted some eclectic events as a growing company such as "Meditation Drinks," "Sex, Yoga, and Rock'n Roll," "First Time Swingers," "Meet, Click, and Eat," and our favorite event "Resolutions Bootcamp." Youlosophy has collaborated with experts from a wide array of disciplines such as artists, athletes, and full-time dreamers. Aiming to reach different audiences beyond our own backyard, we collected our work and published it.

What you have in your hands is the result of our protagonist's journey and the hopeful beginning of yours. Everybody starts somewhere and walks with a unique and fantastic style. Some people choose to fine-tune their entire life all at once, others choose to focus on their goals one at a time. There are those who prefer traditional books, those who enjoy workbooks, and others that go for diaries and planners. No matter the differences, we are all human beings ready to learn and try something new, thus bettering ourselves and the world we live in.

We are all *Youlosophers*.
Diego Mathé
Co-Founder Youlosophy

"Low self-esteem is like driving through life with the parking brake on".

MAXWELL MALTZ

I hadn't realized what self love really was until a few years ago. Since I graduated from high school, I always considered myself someone very capable, someone who with effort could achieve everything. However, I did not realize the little invisible obstacles that were complicating my life. For example, in my jobs, how difficult it was for me to assert myself, negotiate what I wanted or defend my positions when it was clearly easier for others. Socially I was always sensitive to what I felt like criticism, or I always used to cancel invitations at the last minute and thought that "it was part of my character". Not to mention my love life, I was justified in dating people who were inconsiderate of me, shrugging my shoulders like it was all a funny episode of "Sex and the City".

Until someone pointed out to me that they were all signs of low self-esteem, and it was like a revelation. Was it possible that someone like me, apparently so strong and capable, hid a great lack underneath? Discovering this was very hard, but it was also the necessary step to start working on my self-esteem.

Change your relationship with yourself and you will change your world

Relationships, work, free time, food, finances. It was as if all along there had been a better life just there, at my fingertips, waiting for me to claim it as my own.

Why is self love so important? Because it is the vision you have of yourself that allows you to design your life and your well-being. Loving yourself (properly) is the first fundamental step to visualize and build a life that you can truly love.

When you learn to love yourself, your brain gets the message and begins to filter daily what suits you and ignore the rest. On the opposite, when we are low in self-esteem we tend to apply a toxic filter of the world around us and only feed our brain a pessimistic view of things. We miss the opportunities and people who could be good for us. We literally can't see them!

The image you have of yourself is learned throughout your life since you are a baby. This internalized image that you build will depend on what you believe (unconsciously) and influences all the actions of your life: how you react to challenges, failures and successes. Furthermore, the image you have of yourself and the unconscious beliefs will be actually largely responsible for these successes and failures.

For example, if you think you deserve to meet someone, you will generate actions for that to happen even without realizing it. If you feel unworthy, you will do the opposite and read signs of rejection in other people because your brain seeks to confirm your previous belief.

Be the love of your life

If you do not love yourself, but you love others, you generate dependency since your worth is determined by their feedback. If you have low self-esteem, or are angry with yourself, you will reproduce that view of yourself by doing things to cause yourself pain, or by feeling guilty about everything. It is clearly a toxic loop.

Working on your self-esteem does not imply cultivating narcissism but simply accepting yourself and defending your well-being.

Reprogramming your mind for your self-esteem

Even before mindfulness popularized this statement, this was already made clear: you are not your thoughts. It seems obvious but in fact the vast majority of people go through their entire lives identifying with their mind.

Psychology and neuroscience understand that each of us have our own perspective of the world and that this determines how we see everything in our lives. There is a biological reason for this, it is the balance of two of the oldest circuits in our brain: one that alerts you of danger and another that is looking for rewards through new opportunities. You need both to live, and your brain, since you were a baby, has been programming and rewiring itself in favor of one circuit or the other.

One tells you to 'be afraid, don't go out', the other insists that you should 'go outside and look for the new'. The result is your partial way of seeing the world towards the positive or negative aspects of daily life. These biases, how you unconsciously choose to view the world and your life, happen at lightning speed. You are not aware of them, and they are the ones that produce your own skewed version of reality.

This negative view (or bias) often explains why you feel bad, and you can't even put words to the discomfort. Your brain is only teaching you the bad stuff and filtering out all the good stuff.

This choice of vision that your brain makes transforms everything in your life at light speed. Even your health. Have you heard about placebos and nocebos? The famous "placebo effect", widely mentioned by medicine for years, states that a patient can exhibit verifiable physical improvements without any treatment or medication. The fact alone of being convinced that something will do them good achieves this effect. In other words, our minds have tangible effects on our bodies.

The good news. There is scientific evidence that negative bias can be changed through cognitive training, designed to force your brain to see the positive side of things. Our 21-day workbooks have been formulated with this objective in mind. Instead of setting huge goals with a high probability of failing, we dose daily micro-workouts that activate a domino effect and almost imperceptibly replace negative mental patterns with new habits.

Reprogramming is possible

Your brain, while growing up, has been finding shortcuts to the challenges and fears it encountered, and this is the wiring that we must reprogram.

While optimists can benefit from happy and positive thoughts, others with a more catastrophic view of the future have learned to believe that pessimism is an effective protection against everything that can go wrong. Your mind seeks to protect you, and believes that with low expectations, the risk of getting into trouble is lower. Nothing is less true than this!

It is not simply a matter of saying "starting today I will be an optimistic". Our brain has developed a perspective and wiring that has served it well until now, and there are no magic formulas like guided meditations or repeating mantras like "life is beautiful", "the universe loves me" (sorry, Instagram, but we don't believe in you, or love you). In fact, recent studies around the world show that for a person who is suffering from low self-esteem, the "positive meme" or the biased (and posed) posting of people living impossibly wonderful lives, only contributes to internal disqualification and the feeling of worthlessness, failure and isolation. But it is not impossible either. As with anything worthwhile, rewiring your mind requires effort, conviction, and persistence. And you have all this.

Teach yourself and work on yourself

Putting in the time and work to slowly rewire your brain and re-teach it a new worldview is one of the best things you can do for yourself. It is simply that those shortcuts that your brain took many times in the past, no longer work well for you and need to be updated.

The work proposed by this program to rewire your brain and boost your self-esteem is based on four pillars:

· **Self-concept.** The beliefs you have about yourself, how you perceive yourself.
· **Self-image.** How much you like yourself on a personal and physical level.
· **Self-confidence** (also called self-efficacy). The confidence you have in your ability to achieve results or overcome obstacles.
· **Your reinforcements.** The rewards you give yourself and the care you take of your self.

This program will help you detect the areas you need to work on: what you think of yourself, how you see yourself, how you reward yourself and take care of yourself, and what goals you think are possible for you.

For 21 days you will be presented with a series of challenges and exercises. Take note of which are the most difficult ones for you. When you finish with everything, we will ask that you revisit and work specifically on them. One more thing. At Youlosophy we believe in the value of reprogramming and what you can achieve with personal work, but don't rule out consulting with a professional. Working with a therapist allows you to explore your thoughts, feelings, and behavioral patterns, as well as give you tools to manage your symptoms and develop healing strategies.

Remember: your mind can be retrained, but change requires that you picture yourself in a better place or situation than you are in now.

Agustin Marreins
Co-Founder Youlosophy

Neuroplasticity to the rescue!

The main driver for everything we do at Youlosophy is to help people live happy, fulfilled lives. There are countless issues that could be blocking you from achieving the life of your dreams, and most of them are born in your mind.

Both the problems and the solutions reside in the same place: inside your head. The good news is, in the last couple of decades neuroscience has made tremendous progress, and provided us with clues on how to tweak our lives into a happier mode.

Change of any sort, be it learning new skills, discarding old habits and picking up new ones, all have their roots in the brain. Neuroplasticity is the ability of our brain to constantly learn, grow and adapt (not so long ago science believed that after a certain age, brains couldn't change anymore). Neuroplasticity is the key to any world we want to build for ourselves, and it works until our very last breath.

Here's how this works. Every time we learn something, our neurons fire electrochemical signals in a specific pattern and connect with each other. The more often the same pattern is drawn, the faster and easier the connection happens (think of it like a worn grass path after being used as a shortcut daily). Our brain is designed to save energy (which is a survival mechanism), so it will always prefer known shortcuts to new, "risky" and potentially exhausting alternatives.

The same applies to the opposite. The less often a certain pattern shows up on our brain, the weaker it gets (until it eventually disappears). This is how addictions are overcome, but also how we can forget to hug the people we love, or to take some time every day to practice gratitude for all the things we have already.

We are born to life with only a few nerve cells, and these are jumbled. Neuroplasticity forms the basis for our childhood learning processes. Every experience and new skill that we learn multiplies the number of neurons in our brain. Things that took a lot of focus once (like brushing our teeth) eventually go on autopilot, as the neural pattern has been built and strengthened through repetition. Turning useful, positive actions into habits is a great strategy because it frees up your energy to go learn something new, and keep growing and expanding forever (which is, in our humble opinion, a good approach to a happy life).

All Youlosophy programs, regardless of their specific topic, are based on the principle of neuroplasticity. But there's much more to it than repeating an action until it becomes a habit, which is why we resort to several evidence-based methods and combine them in our very own mix. The result is a hands-on approach to mental wellness that works even with people who have little time or no interest in doing therapy (though we still recommend it in many cases).

So here's your key takeaway: your brain is forever malleable, and your choices and daily action affect it and reshape it constantly. This is a powerful and liberating statement, because it gives you the freedom (and the responsibility) to build the life that you want. Nothing is impossible and it's never too late.

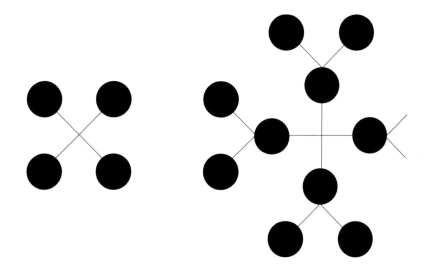

Gratitude

(Ok, so we're rather bad at keeping secrets).
Gratitude is the one common element to any Youlosophy program. Neuroscience studies have shown that a routine of gratitude is most likely to propel your mind and body into an upward spiral.

Among many other benefits, it has been shown that gratitude reduces stress levels, leads to lower depression, makes the heart stronger and healthier and increases emotional well-being. But it also makes you a more effective leader and even more likely to exercise.

Besides all this, we have experienced the positive effects of gratitude firsthand. While there are many ways to exercise it, we have added a gratitude module into our Journal pages, so that for 21 days in a row you will be reminded of reflecting on your day with a focus on the positive. And we encourage you to keep it up once you're done with this book, until it becomes a rock-solid habit. Let's take this gratitude thing for a spin, shall we.

My Gratitude Board

Fill the page with all the things you are grateful for.
Think of the people that in one way or another contributed positively to your life. Think of the places that taught you something, or simply made you happy. You can be thankful for a song, a scent, a memory. Don't filter your thoughts, just let your pen go wild.

❀ When we express gratitude our brain releases dopamine and serotonin, the two crucial neurotransmitters responsible for our emotions. They enhance our mood immediately, making us feel happy from the inside.

How to use
your workbook

Your program is organized into 21 modules. Ideally, you would tackle a module a day, completing your workbook by the end of the third week. This would be wonderful because this collection is called "21 Days" and everything would fit in perfectly (our brain loves that). But it doesn't hurt to accept that life is messy and stuff happens, so we are OK if you take a bit longer to finish your program. You might forget to check in for a few days and then spend the weekend catching-up, and so on.

You get the idea, 21 days is a framework, not a law. However, several neuroscience studies do refer to 3 weeks as the minimum amount of time your brain needs to begin to form a habit (or replace an old one), so make sure to invest at least 21 days in yourself. And we'll take it from there.

Each of the 21 modules ahead is split in two parts. The first triggers action. The second one is aimed at reflection. Just like the heart's movement of systole and diastole, each module promotes expansion and contraction. Step out of your comfort zone for a bit, try something new, ask yourself a question you haven't thought about for a while, then give yourself the time to let it all sink in.

The first part (the Challenge) is where you assess the progress more clearly, while the second (the Journal) is where you build the habit that will get you closer to the life you want.

You will find that the activities in your workbook vary in complexity. Some may even come across as a bit silly (this is intended, so please bear with us and play along). Both parts of a module incorporate techniques that have been used successfully for years.

Your Challenges

A *challenge* is just a new, trendy way of calling something that's been around forever: goals that are measurable and enforce accountability. The **Youlosophy Method** uses the Stages of Change model, which reframes the entire goal-setting process into a series of small, but important, benchmarks (does "tiny habits" ring a bell?). So consider each Daily Challenge a small, yet powerful step towards achieving your ultimate goal.

Try to complete one challenge everyday.
Keep a pencil or pen handy! Your workbook pages are meant to be written and doodled on!

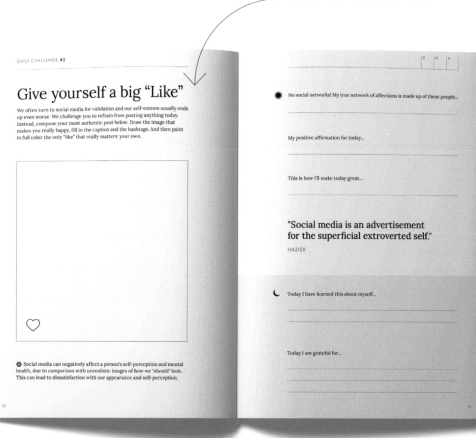

Give yourself a big "Like"

We often turn to social media for validation and our self-esteem usually ends up even worse. We challenge you to refrain from posting anything today. Instead, compose your most authentic post below. Draw the image that makes you really happy, fill in the caption and the hashtags. And then paint in full color the only "like" that really matters: your own.

❤

Social media can negatively affect a person's self-perception and mental health, due to comparison with unrealistic images of how we "should" look. This can lead to dissatisfaction with our appearance and self-perception.

D M A

No social networks! My true network of affections is made up of these people...

My positive affirmation for today...

This is how I'll make today great...

"Social media is an advertisement for the superficial extroverted self."
HAZIER

Today I have learned this about myself...

Today I am grateful for...

Your Journal

Journaling is a scientifically-proven method of rewiring your brain to focus on the tasks that matter and avoiding any distractions that cause stress and negativity. **While the Challenges encourage action, and stepping out of your comfort zone, it is the Journal which does the trick of rewiring your brain and transforming your life.** During your program you will tackle 21 different exercises, but you will focus your thoughts on exactly the same stuff for that long until this will eventually come natural to you.

What if you asked yourself an identical question for 21 days? Would the answer be always the same?

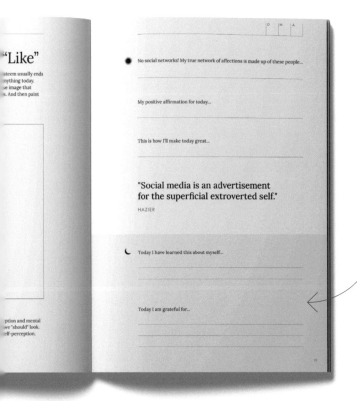

Most of our Journals include a section for Affirmations and a Gratitude Log. Affirmations are very specific sentences that express a wish in the present tense and always in a positive format. There are no "I won't miss any workouts" but instead "I make it to every workout".

We will sometimes suggest a specific affirmation, related to that day's activity, but we encourage you to come up with your own, and repeat them daily for the entire length of the program. There is scientific evidence that our brain has no way to distinguish between reality and an alternative scenario that is presented as real to it. By applying **visualization** daily, or rather at several times a day, the brain will be able to take the steps necessary to achieve your result in both a conscious and unconscious state.

My positive affirmation of the day

_____

_____

_____

_____

Today I am grateful for

_____

_____

_____

Your journal ends the same way every day: with a **gratitude log**. You've read about this practice a few pages back, but we can't emphasize it enough. As covered in the New York Times, "gratitude stimulates the hypothalamus (a key part of the brain that regulates stress) and the ventral tegmental area (part of our "reward circuitry" that produces the sensation of pleasure). There you have it, scientific proof.

Now, let's turn the page and make some magic.

Digital Detox!

Whether you're working on finding your true voice, boosting your self-esteem, or igniting joy in your life, reducing your social media consumption will help you focus and put things in perspective.

🕐 Pick a time of the day to visit your digital world .... : ....

⏳ Limit your online activity to 30 minutes a day

🔔 Turn off notifications from social media

🗑 Pick one social media app and delete it for a month

▦ App to be deleted _____

📅 Date deleted .... / .... / ....

⚛ Social media robs us of our ability to be productive, empathetic and original. A digital detox improves personal well-being and reduces symptoms of loneliness and depression.

✴ Today I say #seeyoulater to social networks. I will dedicate this extra time to...

_____

My positive affirmation of the day...

_____

Today I will focus on...

_____

"Facebook is to mental health, what fossil fuel is to climate health."

ABHIJIT NASKAR

☾ Today I have learned this about myself...

_____

_____

🙌 Today I am grateful for...

_____

_____

_____

Give yourself a big "Like"

We often turn to social media for validation and our self-esteem usually ends up even worse. We challenge you to refrain from posting anything today. Instead, compose your most authentic post below. Draw the image that makes you really happy, fill in the caption and the hashtags. And then paint in full color the only "like" that really matters: your own.

❀ Social media can negatively affect a person's self-perception and mental health, due to comparison with unrealistic images of how we "should" look. This can lead to dissatisfaction with our appearance and self-perception.

✸ No social networks! My true network of affections is made up of these people...

_____

My positive affirmation for today...

_____

This is how I'll make today great...

_____

"Social media is an advertisement for the superficial extroverted self."

HAZIER

🌙 Today I have learned this about myself...

_____

_____

🙌 Today I am grateful for...

_____

_____

_____

Tear off those labels

Fill in the labels on the left with your negative beliefs about yourself. Then rewrite them on the right in a more objective and self-compassionate way. For example: **"I'm dumb"** can be replaced with **"I don't know everything, but I'm always learning"**.

Several studies show that negative labels (assigned by others, but especially self-generated ones) contribute to low self-esteem and feelings of helplessness, and are related to high levels of stigma and depression.

✺ The word that defines the best of me today is...

_____

My positive affirmation for today...

_____

This is how I'll make today great...

_____

"I don't like labels. They limit you, and I don't want limits."

MADONNA

☾ Today I have learned this about myself...

_____

_____

🙌 Today I am grateful for...

_____

_____

_____

Nothing compares to you

There will always be someone younger, stronger, more something than ourselves. Would you suggest to a friend that she compares herself to the beauty of Miss Universe? Do you compare your father's good fortune to that of Bill Gates? Or your son's sporting prowess versus Christiano Ronaldo's? Well, we do submit to these cruel comparisons every day.

Who do you compare yourself to sometimes? List them below. Then write down the aspects that make you two completely different persons, with different opportunities and abilities. Explain to your mind once and for all why that comparison is useless and end the debate.

Comparison

Differences

The negative influence of social networks on humanity's self-esteem is widely proven. The greater the use of social networks, the greater the tendency to believe that others have happier lives, and are better off in all aspects of their lives (Chou & Edge, 2012; de Vries & Kühne, 2015).

✷ I can only compare myself to myself. And compared to yesterday, today I feel...

_____

My positive affirmation for today...

_____

This is how I'll make today great...

_____

"You're always with yourself, so you might as well enjoy the company."

JON FOREMAN

☾ Today I have learned this about myself...

_____

_____

🙌 Today I am grateful for...

_____

_____

_____

Nobody is perfect

Setting high goals helps us grow. But if they are not realistic we are only condemning ourselves to failure. Practice flexibility daily to keep perfectionism at bay.

1. Describe a problem you have faced recently.

2. Think about how a person you admire would have handled it, if they were in your place.

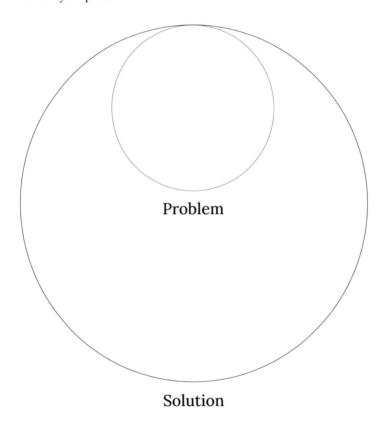

Problem

Solution

⚛ Recent studies at universities in the US have shown that students who are more open to trying new things and making mistakes obtained better academic grades at the end of their studies.

✸ Here's someone who truly loves me and this is what he/she thinks of me...

_____

My positive affirmation for today...

_____

This is how I'll make today great...

_____

"If only you could perceive how important you are to the lives of those who come across you. You leave something of yourself in each person who knows you, don't forget it."

FRED ROGERS

☾ Today I have learned this about myself...

_____

_____

🙌 Today I am grateful for...

_____

_____

_____

How do you see the glass?

Although the future does not exist (only the present moment), our minds love to make predictions. Pessimism is the tendency to predict negative outcomes, and carries the risk of "filtering" events, hiding opportunities, and becoming a self-fulfilling prophecy. The vast majority of the time things do not turn out as badly as a pessimist expects.

See for yourself! Write down your predictions for today, this month, and the rest of the year. Set an alarm on your calendar to check back later.

⚛ Pessimists have a greater tendency to believe that things happen because of their responsibility rather than because of an external situation. Every time you prove your predictions wrong, you train your brain to see yourself from a different perspective. Over time you will begin to interpret your limitations and capabilities in a more accurate and healthy way.

D   M   Y

☀ I choose optimism! Today will be...

_____

My positive affirmation for today...

_____

This is how I'll make today great...

_____

"Choose to be optimistic, it feels better."

DALAI LAMA

☾ Today I love myself a bit more because...

_____
_____

🙌 Today I am grateful for...

_____
_____
_____

Put that whip away

People who have a low self-esteem find it hard to recognize their achievements. A typical attitude: when you achieve something, you attribute it to luck, but if you fail then you feel totally responsible. This way you increase your insecurity and it is very difficult for you to develop self-esteem.

Keep track of your negative evaluations throughout the day. How many times do you think negatively of yourself daily? In what situations? What do you think?

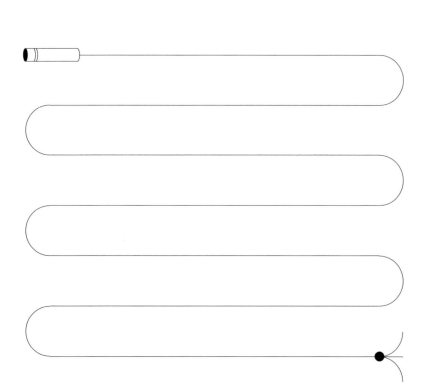

It has been shown (Kilduff, 2013) that a person's thoughts and feelings upon entering a group determine their status within it in the long term. People who felt and behaved as happy or energetic, acquired a higher status and recognition in a group.

✳ I will begin to look at myself with fairness and moderation. What respectful and affectionate adjectives suit me today?

_____

My positive affirmation for today...

_____

This is how I'll make today great...

_____

"The man who does not value himself, cannot value anything or anyone."

AYN RAND

☾ Today I love myself a bit more because...

_____

_____

_____

¡Today I've done _____!

I deserve a big bear hug from myself.

The Weekly Check-in

Time to take a pause and reflect on the week that was.

My score for
this past week is: (1) (2) (3) (4) (5) (6) (7) (8) (9) (10)

Why?

_____

_____

_____

These were the
three highest points
of my week:

```
        ┌──────┐
        │  1   │
    ┌───┤      │
    │ 2 │      ├──────┐
    │   │      │  3   │
    │   │      │      │
    │   │      │      │
    └───┴──────┴──────┘
```

These were the
three lowest points
of my week:

```
    ┌──────┬──────┐
    │      │      │
    │      │      ├──────┐
    │  2   │      │  3   │
    │      │      │      │
    └──────┤  1   │      │
           │      │
           └──────┘
```

The most important person of my week
(besides myself) was:

What touched me?

_____

_____

_____

What made me upset?

_____

_____

_____

What did I do for myself?

_____

_____

_____

What can I do next week to get closer to my ideal life?

_____

_____

_____

You are as strong as you feel

Today we'd like you to focus on your strongest points and fill the arm below with some positive tattoos!

The truth is, you're quite awesome. But there's always room for a little improvement. What aspects would you like to work on?

✿ According to Positive Psychology, emphasizing people's abilities and potential can make people happier and more satisfied with their lives.

✳ One word that describes me today

My positive affirmation for today...

This is how I'll make today great...

"Every weakness contains within itself a strength."

SHUSAKU ENDO

☾ This is what made today awesome

🙌 Today I am grateful for...

What do you see when you look at yourself?

We all know by now that true beauty lies inside. But it doesn't hurt that you also reconcile with your body.

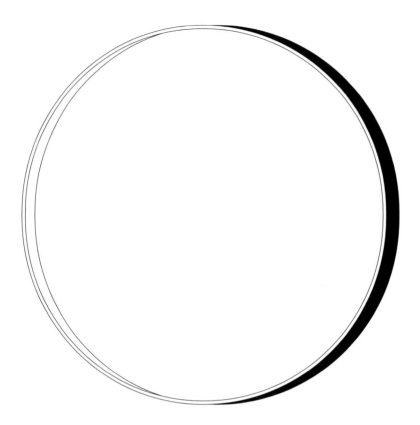

A 2016 study of 160 college students found that 79% were dissatisfied with their bodies. A low body image often leads to eating disorders or mental health problems. Social media is highly toxic in this regard.

✸ What is my most beautiful feature?

_____

My positive affirmation for today...

_____

This is how I'll make today great...

_____

"Choose to be optimistic, it feels better."

DALAI LAMA

☾ How did I feel today?

DAZZLING   INVISIBLE   SHEER BEAUTY   SAME AS ALWAYS

BETTER THAN BEFORE   CHANGING   IN FREE FALL

In my own words _____

🙌 Today I am grateful for...

_____

_____

You deserve an applause!

Children are celebrated for any progress, even if far from perfection. When was the last time you congratulated yourself on something? The first step to healthy self-esteem is to recognize your achievements, and stop punishing yourself for your mistakes.

Fill in the space below with things you have done well in your life.
Huge, small, a long time ago or just yesterday.

This is a cognitive behavioral therapy technique that teaches your mind to change the way you think. Several studies verify that this has a physical effect on people's brains.

✹ What challenge will I take on today?

My positive affirmation for today...

This is how I'll make today great...

"You've been criticizing yourself for years, and it hasn't borne good fruit. Try to show yourself approval, see what happens."

LOUISE L. HAY

☾ What things, no matter how simple or routine, have I done well today?

🙌 Today I am grateful for...

Let's put things in perspective

Here's a common formula for frustration or depression: we evaluate successes externally -"I got it thanks to luck"-, but failures internally -"This has gone wrong because of me." Let's change these views that damage you. Make a list below:

Things that you have achieved and have depended on you.

Things that didn't turn out the way you wanted but really weren't your responsibility.

_____

_____

_____

_____

_____

_____

_____

_____

_____

❀ If you evaluate everything from an external perspective, then nothing depends on you, neither the successes nor the failures, and this paralyzes you. If you evaluate everything internally -I am responsible for everything that happens to me- then you are also responsible for everything bad that happens to you, or what doesn't work out or happens in your life. The key here lies, once again, in finding balance.

✹ I start the day thanking myself, especially for...

_____

My positive affirmation for today...

_____

This is how I'll make today great...

_____

"You are not your mistakes. They are what you did, not who you are."

LISA LIEBERMAN WANG

☾ Today I am my own fan! And I say this because...

_____

_____

🖐🖐 Today I am grateful for...

_____

_____

_____

Sweet (self)talk

Do you praise yourself when you do something well? Or do you forget about your achievements but punish yourself for your failures?
Today we want you to keep a record (use this page) of the things you do well (even if they are minimal, like getting up on time or finishing a pending task). Write down each achievement and add a little congratulations note next to it.

Achievement   Congratulation

_____   _____

_____   _____

_____   _____

_____   _____

_____   _____

_____   _____

_____   _____

_____   _____

_____   _____

We invite you to continue this practice for several days. You may take am empty notebook and always carry it with you. We recommend that you do not use a mobile phone for this task.

❀ Studies in patients with depression and PTSD (Schou, 2017) show that changing thoughts and habits visibly improves wellbeing and has physically increased the connections of the amygdala with regions of the brain that control cognitive functions. **Rewriting your thoughts and retraining your brain is, indeed, possible.**

☀ A compliment I would like to say to myself every day is...

_____

My positive affirmation for today...

_____

This is how I'll make today great...

_____

"You are imperfect, permanently and inevitably imperfect. And you're beautiful."

AMY BLOOM

🌙 I have reached the end of the day! This alone deserves a...

_____

_____

🙌 Today I am grateful for...

_____

_____

_____

That pesky voice inside

Eliminating the "I am not capable" and modifying that toxic internal dialogue are key tasks in the development of our self-esteem. Find that voice inside that tends to diminish you and change its tune already! Every time you find yourself thinking "I won't be able to do it" whisper to yourself "enough", "stop", "no more" and change the activity you were doing. This constant exercise will rewrite your brain.

Let's start putting this into practice. Make a list of the good things you have done and achieved in life. We are going to start introducing your brain to your best version, so that next time it trusts you a little more.

The positive results of Cognitive Behavior Therapies have been demonstrated in recent years (Hoffman, 2012). The idea is not to think "positively" but "realistically".

✸ I'll name that voice in my head "_____"

and I'll let it know I'm much better than he/she thinks!

My positive affirmation for today...

_____

This is how I'll make today great...

_____

"You are either as beautiful or as ugly as you believe you are. You define your beauty. That's not a power anyone can have over you."

AUTHOR UNKNOWN

☾ I sense a great day is coming! I deserve it because...

_____

_____

🙌 Today I am grateful for...

_____

_____

_____

Know how to lose

We learn through our mistakes. This implies that your failures are, at the end of the day, more valuable than your successes. But beware, this is only valid if you know how to lose, which is when your emotions do not prevent your brain from capitalizing on the mistake and continuing to learn. List below the failures that helped you learn a lesson. What happened? What did you learn?

_____

_____

_____

_____

_____

_____

_____

_____

_____

_____

_____

_____

_____

_____

_____

_____

❀ Parents who always let their children win out of fear of hurting their self-esteem are in fact depriving them of the valuable lessons that come with failing.

✴ Today I free myself from this toxic self-demand...

_____

My positive affirmation for today...

_____

This is how I'll make today great...

_____

"The life of a man is interesting mainly if he has failed. That indicates that he tried to outdo himself."

GEORGES CLEMENCEAU

☾ Today I made this mistake, which will help me be better tomorrow...

_____

_____

🤲 Today I am grateful for...

_____

_____

_____

The Weekly Check-in

Time to take a pause and reflect on the week that was.

My score for
this past week is: ① ② ③ ④ ⑤ ⑥ ⑦ ⑧ ⑨ ⑩

Why?

_____

_____

_____

These were the
three highest points
of my week:

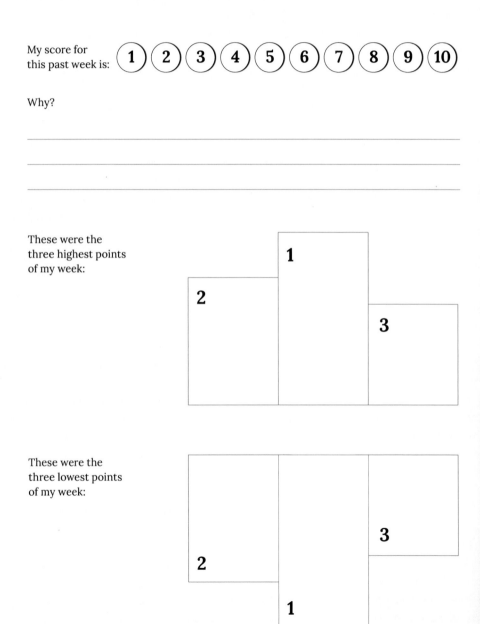

These were the
three lowest points
of my week:

The most important person of my week
(besides myself) was:

What touched me?

_____

_____

_____

What made me upset?

_____

_____

_____

What did I do for myself?

_____

_____

_____

What can I do next week to get closer to my ideal life?

_____

_____

_____

Yes, you can!

Prepare to read something you already know. Confidence is key to achieving your goals. Pushing yourself too little is just as harmful as pushing yourself too hard, so tread carefully.

Your challenge today is to better understand your skills and knowledge, and see them objectively. Make a list below (first, in no particular order) of your abilities. Next, assign a score to each item on the list, 1 being the highest grade.

- ☐ _____
- ☐ _____
- ☐ _____
- ☐ _____
- ☐ _____
- ☐ _____
- ☐ _____
- ☐ _____
- ☐ _____
- ☐ _____
- ☐ _____

Do you use these abilities frequently? Make sure to study or work in fields that put your biggest strengths to work. Can you think of a different activity where you could deploy them to a larger extent?

✤ Some scientists endorse the Power Pose technique advocated by Amy Cuddy (2010) in her TED talk. She affirms that assuming a position that you consider powerful minutes before an interaction in which you need more confidence in yourself, will bring positive results in your life.

✳ My greatest ability is _____

And today I will use it in this situation _____

My positive affirmation for today...

_____

This is how I'll make today great...

_____

"Too many people overvalue what they are not and undervalue what they are."

MALCOLM S. FORBES

☾ Today I have learned this about myself...

_____

_____

🙌 Today I am grateful for...

_____

_____

_____

Design your alter ego

Imagine an alternative version of yourself. It can be whoever you want, but it must be the opposite of your fears. Stand in front of the mirror and visualize yourself being that person. Get in character and talk like this person, until you feel like your own in front of the mirror. The more you practice, the more you will incorporate it.

Describe your alternate self in detail. What aspects of your alter ego would you want for yourself? How could you reach them?

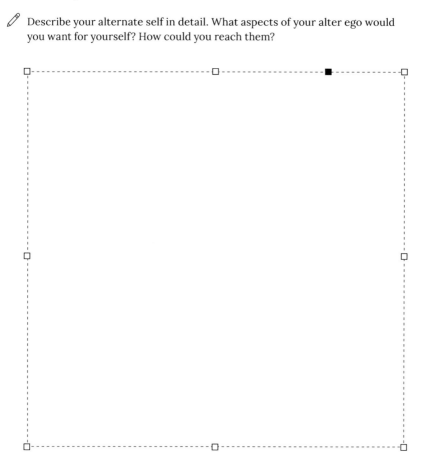

⚘ Many artists develop what is known as an alter-ego in order to get on stage, face crowds, or compete in sports. This other part of you is called your "Heroic Self", and you reveal it with an Alter Ego. Author Todd Herman argues that you can use your alter ego to achieve the previously impossible. It's worth a try!

✸ Today I will get closer to my ideal Self, which is...

_____

My positive affirmation for today...

_____

This is how I'll make today great...

_____

"I pretended to be somebody I wanted to be until finally, I became that person. Or he became me."

CARY GRANT

☾ I score the day that ended with a _____ for the following reasons...

_____

_____

🙌 Today I am grateful for...

_____

_____

_____

Time for yourself

We live in a culture that idealizes productivity, and we have become used to delaying gratification, even though it is fundamental to showing self-esteem. If you do not block and respect some time for yourself, there will always be someone or something that seems urgent and cannot be postponed.

🖊 What would you do if you had a free hour today? And two hours next week? What would a weekend designed just for you be like? Write in all down in as much detail as possible.

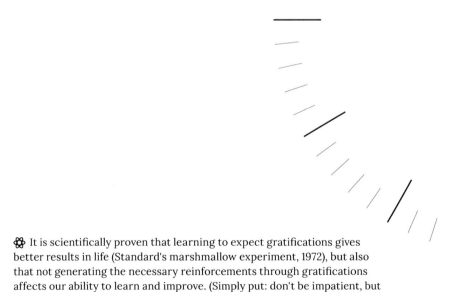

❀ It is scientifically proven that learning to expect gratifications gives better results in life (Standard's marshmallow experiment, 1972), but also that not generating the necessary reinforcements through gratifications affects our ability to learn and improve. (Simply put: don't be impatient, but allow yourself your rewards when they're due.)

☀ Today I decide that I deserve the following reward

_____

Which will be given to me on this date _____

My positive affirmation for today...

_____

This is how I'll make today great...

_____

"A healthy self-love means we have no compulsion to justify to ourselves or others why we take vacations, why we sleep late, why we buy new shoes, why we spoil ourselves from time to time. We feel comfortable doing things which add quality and beauty to life."

ANDREW MATTHEWS

☾ Today I am grateful for...

_____

_____

_____

Praise yourself

While you may not always give yourself due recognition for your victories, it is possible to build this habit. In the short term, your internal dialogue can make you feel better or worse. But it's what happens under the surface that matters most:

We are going to put self-praise into practice with a very simple (and well-known) exercise. Imagine you are a "product" for sale and write an ad to promote yourself. While lies and exaggeration are not allowed, we do encourage you to highlight all your positive virtues.

your face here

⚘ Praise activates the striatum, one of the brain areas associated with rewards and reinforcement. Studies (Sugawara, 2012) have proven that praise enhances the learning that occurs during sleep (skill consolidation).

✳ I start the day with praise for myself.

I love myself because I am _____ , _____ and _____

And although some may say I'm a bit _____
I love myself just like this.

My positive affirmation for today...

_____

This is how I'll make today great...

_____

"Until you value yourself, you will not value your time. Until you value your time, you won't do anything with it."

M. SCOTT PECK

☾ Today I love myself a little more than yesterday, because...

_____

_____

🤲 Today I am grateful for...

_____

_____

_____

Your ability to feel

Connecting with our ability to feel strengthens our self-esteem and the bond with ourselves. Today we challenge you to take your workbook out to the street and keep a perceptive/subjective record of everything that your senses catch.

What draws your attention? What do you see? What do you hear? What do you smell? Superpower your senses, make a conscious effort so you don't miss anything. List what you perceive and then, next to it, how it makes you feel.

⊛ Connecting with the present, with reality, is easier in nature. Also called grounding, several studies (ie. Bowen, 2016) have shown the power of going outdoors, and connecting with nature in strengthening resilience and self-love.

☀ Today I will reward myself with my favorite flavor, which is _____

And I'll start the day with my favorite song _____

My positive affirmation for today...

_____

This is how I'll make today great...

_____

"I go to nature to be soothed and healed, and to have my senses put in order."

THE DARK SIDE OF THE HEART

☾ Today my senses have given me this gift...

_____

_____

🙌 Today I am grateful for...

_____

_____

_____

Explore and grow!

Although we believe we dread it, we choose routine because our brain seeks security. We get used to having a predictable life, which gives us confidence and decreases energy expenditure, but we lose the ability to explore. And it is the game, the ability to explore, to feel, sniff and investigate the new that leads to the greatest satisfaction.

How long has it been since you tried something new that forced you out of your comfort zone? What activities have you been postponing for years?

⚘ Dopamine controls mental and emotional responses, as well as motor reactions. It is often called the "happiness hormone", and it is responsible for our happy experiences. Adrenaline, which is triggered by physical actions, sports or exposure to risk, is associated with it and based on the same pattern. But the production of too little or too much dopamine can cause health problems.

☀ Today I will take a stroll outside my comfort zone. And I will...

_____

My positive affirmation for today...

_____

This is how I'll make today great...

_____

"Be strong enough to face the world each day. Be weak enough to know you cannot do everything alone."

AUTHOR UNKNOWN

☾ And soon I will also dare...

_____

_____

🙌 Today I am grateful for...

_____

_____

_____

Yellow Brick Road of Dreams

It's time to help your brain visualize the life you want! Without too much thinking fill each of the sticky notes with a goal or dream.

When you visualize something you take a big first step towards making it real. It sounds like science fiction, but it's just science.

✳ The thing I wish for most today is...

_____

My positive affirmation for today...

_____

Today I will focus on...

_____

"The future belongs to those who believe in the beauty of their dreams."

ELEANOR ROOSEVELT

☾ Today I learned this about myself...

_____

_____

🙌 Today I am grateful for...

_____

_____

_____

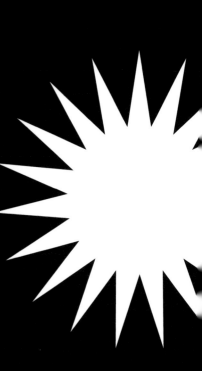

Congratulations!

You have reached the debrief section.

Your daily challenges are all done now, and it is time to take some conclusions before moving on (because there is not a doubt that you will want to continue, although only you will decide when and in what direction).

Hidden in the 21 activities you have completed are the connections, thoughts and associations that most affect your self-esteem. Identifying your specific problem areas is key to focusing on them during your next growth program.

For instance, there are people with self-esteem problems who have great selfconfidence. Others may give themselves good reinforcements, rewards and care (pampering) but still have a self-image problem. For others the problem is their ability to set goals for growth. Or the body perception, or the lack of self-praise, or an insufficient gratitude time with themselves.

Go back to your workbook pages and mark those exercises that offered the most resistance to you. Re-read your journal entries, red pen in hand, and underline common patterns. You are a detective deciphering what your mind does not want you to know. Highlight the challenges, the blockages, what you left incomplete. That's where your greatest growth opportunity lies.

Now answer these questions:

In what ways do you believe that self-esteem problems affect your life?

_____

_____

_____

_____

_____

_____

_____

_____

Think of a better place. What would happen if you solved the self-esteem problems that you have detected?

_____

_____

_____

_____

_____

_____

_____

_____

_____

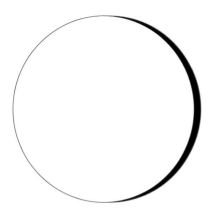

What is still going through your head?
What do you feel that you haven't
been able to understand yet?

What have you managed to grasp?
What do you really understand?

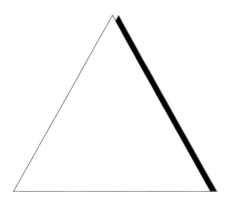

List three conclusions that you have drawn
and that you will put into practice in your life.

More debrief...

Based on what you have learned these days: What will you start doing and what things will you stop doing? What will you continue to do? How will you change what you are doing?

Start

_____
_____
_____
_____
_____
_____
_____
_____

Stop

_____
_____
_____
_____
_____
_____
_____
_____

Continue

_____
_____
_____
_____
_____
_____
_____

Change

_____
_____
_____
_____
_____
_____
_____

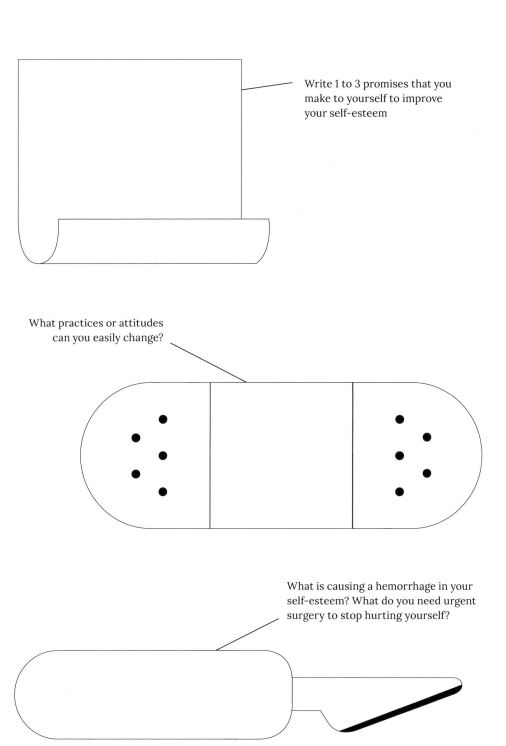

Write 1 to 3 promises that you make to yourself to improve your self-esteem

What practices or attitudes can you easily change?

What is causing a hemorrhage in your self-esteem? What do you need urgent surgery to stop hurting yourself?

Personal Growth
Made Easy

Developed by experts and inspired by you, our programs and journals combine neuroscience-based exercises with journaling and mindfulness prompts. Each one helps develop skills for a happier and more fulfilled life.

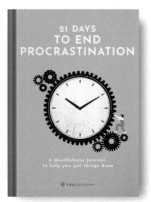

Now that you have completed this plan, there is no doubt you will want to go for more. The question is, where does your journey go from here?

Our special recommendation for you

Your life is unique, just like you. No one should tell you what's next, that choice is completely yours. Our catalog covers various topics of personal development, and you will surely find inspiration to continue your journey.

The program you have completed touches, albeit only on the surface, on the question of spirituality, your connection to everything around you, and the role visualisation plays in fulfilling your dreams. If you are interested in exploring these subjects more in depth, we recommend our plan "**21 Days to Abundance**".

You will find these and **more titles at youlosophy.com** and in selected shops.

Resources
for your Journey

The Daily Stoic: 366 Meditations on Wisdom, Perseverance, and the Art of Living (Ryan Holiday y Stephen Hanselman)

Behave: The Biology of Humans at Our Best and Worst (Robert M Sapolsky)

Dopamine Nation: Finding Balance in the Age of Indulgence (Dr Anna Lembke)

The Happiness Hypothesis: Finding Modern Truth in Ancient Wisdom (Jonathan Haidt)

Descartes' Error: Emotion, Reason and the Human Brain (Antonio R. Damasio)

Smart World: Breakthrough Creativity And the New Science of Ideas (Richard Ogle)

The Blank Slate: The Modern Denial of Human Nature (Steven Pinker)

Consilience: The Unity of Knowledge (Edward O. Wilson)

Seven and a Half Lessons About the Brain (Lisa Feldman Barrett)

A Million Things To Ask A Neuroscientist: The brain made easy (Mike Tranter PhD)

101 Essays That Will Change The Way You Think (Brianna Wiest)

The Science of Love and Attraction: The long-hidden neurobiological secrets to improve your social and romantic life (Mehmet Oktar Guloglu Ph.D.)

The 48 Laws of Power (Robert Greene)

How Emotions Are Made: The Secret Life of the Brain (Lisa Feldman Barrett)

 MANY MORE ON YOULOSOPHY.COM

All our Gratitude

To everybody involved in the creation
and distribution of this program.

Many thanks to every person (past and
present) on the Youlosophy team.
To our investors, partners
and business associates.

And especially to you, for trusting us
and inspiring us to continue growing
and improving every day.

Credits

First edition: December 2021
@ Youlosophy SL, 2021
Carrer Diputació 50
08015, Barcelona, Spain
www.youlosophy.com